Woody, the Kentucky Wiener

Tails from the Bluegrass II

by

Leigh Anne Florence

Illustrations by
James Asher

Cover design and book layout by Asher Graphics
Illustrations by James Asher

Manufactured in the United States of America

All book order correspondence should be addressed to:

HotDiggetyDog Press
P.O. Box 747
Shepherdsville, KY 40165

502-543-5315
ronandleigh@alltel.net
www.thewoodybooks.com

Dedication

This book is dedicated to James Asher – the best illustrator in the whole wide world. We keep thinking your illustrations can't get any better, but guess what? They do! Nobody can illustrate a wiener dog, a bookmobile, or white horse like you! Thanks for bringing our stories to life!

Foreword

For children, reading can be such an exciting experience, opening windows to places unseen and giving complete license to the imagination. Reading about animals is a comfortable connection for children, so helping them "see" their state and all its wonderful resources and vistas through the eyes of two adventuresome dachshunds is the best of all literary worlds.

Kentucky is so wonderfully rich in places to visit, both indoors and out. A local resident or a visitor from far away will find something to enjoy in the historic buildings, parklands, rivers, architecture, museums, special events, and timeless traditions displayed in every county and every corner of the Commonwealth.

It's important for everyone to find ways for children to be engaged in what Kentucky has to offer, as they will be the ones framing the future and determining the value placed on preserving what defines it now and what will be its definition in the decades to come.

By describing our past and present in *Tails From the Bluegrass II*, Woody and Chloe are pointing out the pathway to our future for children of any age. Dreaming like a big dog will take them there.

Kadie Engstrom
Education Coordinator
Belle of Louisville

Woody would like to thank...

Mom, Dad, and Chloe. You are the greatest family any wiener dog could ask for. Thanks for taking care of me and loving me – even when I am in the dog-house!

The WOODY TEAM – Lori, Sue, Nathan, and Shaun! Your hard work behind the scenes allows Chloe and me to shine!

The great ladies at McClanahan Publishing – Paula, Michelle, and Jo. We always love the finished product!

Our friends at Kentucky Press – David, Kriss, Bekki, Jennifer, and Kevin. Thanks for giving us this great opportunity! We love seeing our stories in print each week!

Louisville Gas & Electric/Kentucky Utilities –
E.ON U.S. – especially Mr. Cliff and Mr. Chris;
Mr. Gene Wilhoit and the Kentucky Department
of Education; and Kentucky First Lady Glenna
Fletcher (say 'Arff" to Abby!).

Uncle Guy for his fine proofreading skills.

Carla and her girls for getting the ball rolling.

The 85 Kentucky newspapers and all the schools
who participated in the "Tails" series. Hope you
enjoy making the journey again!

And finally, to you — our friends — for reading
our books, attending our events, sending us kind
letters and emails, and giving us sweet hugs and
kisses on the road! Chloe and I love that, so
please don't ever stop!

Enjoy the TAILS...

Chapter 1

On the road again,
I just can't wait to get on the road again,
Dah, Dah, Tah, Dah…

Hip, Hip Hooray! Yippee! I am so excited! I have to find my Scooby suitcase and start packing! I couldn't believe my dog ears when the newspaper called and asked if I would take another "Tour of the Bluegrass!" "Another Woody Tour – you mean like an 'encore' performance?" I asked. "That's right, Woody! We want you and your family to travel around the great Commonwealth of Kentucky. Please keep a good diary and tell us what you find. We will post your weekly journal in the newspaper and of course we will pay you for your work!" The newspaper office didn't have to ask me twice. "I will put my paw print on the dotted line right now." Of course there were *de TAILS* to work out – the usual questions like, "When do we leave? Should my work be in type or in paw print? Will I be paid in coins or Milk Bones?" The important part is that Dad is loading the Woody Bus right now and Woody, The Kentucky Wiener is coming to your town!

I'm sorry! Where are my manners? I should introduce myself to the folks I haven't met! My name is Dogwood, but my friends call me Woody. I'm a seven-year-old black and tan miniature dachshund, or wiener dog, and was born and raised in Kentucky. (Hence the name "Woody, The Kentucky Wiener!") Chloe is my sister. She's eight years old and is a red-headed wiener dog. She's beautiful – and the best big sister ever. We live in Shepherdsville, Kentucky with Mom and Dad. We also have two brothers (Rio, a Labrador retriever and Little Bit, a cat) and two sisters (Cheyenne, another Lab and Dolly, another cat). Though we love our Shepherdsville doghouse, it seems like we are quite the traveling hot dogs. You see, Mom writes books about us. (Who knew there was a demand for books about wiener dogs?) To our surprise, not only did people read the books, but my phone started ringing. "Woody, can you come to our school and talk about hard work and goal setting?" Now that I could do. You see, my life hasn't always been easy. I was born the runt of the litter, or the underdog as I like to think. The owner of the Paducah, Kentucky farm didn't think I would amount to anything since I was so tiny, yet one day a lady and her wiener dog came to rescue me. That lady turned out to be Mom and that wiener dog turned out to be Chloe. That was the best day of my life. Our family has definitely grown since that beautiful April day in 1999, and so has my confidence. Mom and Dad have always told Chloe and me that we could do anything we put our mind to, but

we have to set goals and work hard to reach those goals. We have to "Work and Dream like a BIG DOG!"

Well, if writing books and speaking in schools wasn't exciting enough, last year the newspaper asked if I would travel around and report what I saw. They didn't ask me to stay in Kentucky, but it is such a beautiful state that I didn't want to go anywhere else. Therefore, Chloe, Mom, Dad, and I spent weeks on the road in our Woody Bus visiting all sorts of neat places like Pikeville, Bowling Green, Wickliffe, Monkey's Eyebrow, just to name a few. We had a blast! I guess the newspaper people were impressed since they have asked us to do it all again. Therefore, here we are, suitcases packed, ready to come to your town. In fact, Mom, Dad, and Chloe are downstairs waiting on me, so I better run before Dad has to come up the stairs, call me Dogwood, and tell me to get my tail moving. Uh oh... too late... here he is.

"Woody, bad news."

"I know Dad. Sorry I'm wagging behind."

"No Woody. That's not what I am talking about. The bad news is that the Woody Bus will not start!"

"It won't start? Oh no! Did you use the key like you always do? Maybe it is thirsty!"

"Woody, I know how to start the bus and yes, it has plenty of gas. It just won't start. We are going to have to talk about the tour!"

Oh no, was the tour over before we ever left the driveway? I guess we will have to wait and see. In the meantime, don't give up hope and Work and Dream like a BIG DOG!

Chapter 2

"You get a line, I'll get a pole, Honey!
You get a line...

Kentucky Greetings, Woody Readers! Please excuse my singing, but I am *PAWS-atively* excited to be on tour! Mom, Dad, Chloe, and I are in the Woody Bus, I mean, Woody BOAT, traveling down the river! "Why a boat? Remember when Dad told me the Woody Bus wouldn't start? Dad tried everything, but nothing worked." Chloe and I were afraid the tour would be canceled, but Mom reminded us winners didn't give up. "Woody, how do you think people traveled before cars?" Mom asked. "I thought cars had ALWAYS been around! I was born in 1999 and they were around then!" I said. Chloe giggled and pointed out how Granddaddy told us about walking three miles to school every day in rain and snow. Sure, that was fine for Granddad. He was in great shape, but I couldn't walk the Woody Tour! I could run fast when chasing butterflies, and could even flex my muscles (sniff, sniff), but long distances were a different story! I was getting worried when Chloe said, "Hey! The Salt River is just down the road! We

know plenty of fishermen who could help!" I kissed my sister for saving the day!

Dad unloaded the bus and Mom instructed us to pack the necessities. "Woody, your *GameDOG* is NOT a necessity!" I obeyed Mom and packed my Scooby journal, pencils, Kentucky map, and toothbrush!

We hugged our siblings and headed south on Highway 61 to the Salt River. It was two miles from home to the river bank. While walking, I made a note to self to start exercising more. Two miles were challenging. The boat was a super idea, but it would be tough to make the entire tour by boat. My thoughts were interrupted when we reached the Salt River and saw our buddy, Mr. Sullivan, in his flat-bottom fishing boat. We told Mr. Sullivan about our problem with the bus. He was more than happy to help. "Which way are you going?" Tough question! Dad explained the Salt River was 140 miles long. It began near Danville and ended at the Ohio River near West Point. West it was! We buckled our life jackets and settled in our seats. Mr. Sullivan put the oars in the water and off we sailed!

Mr. Sullivan was no stranger to the Salt River. His great-granddad sailed the river to get to Pitts Point. Once a town in Bullitt County, Pitts Point was used by people to ship salt produced by Bullitt's Lick. It even had a college. After the Civil War, Pitts Point Academy was known as one of the best schools in Central Kentucky. Unfortunately, today Pitts Point is just a memory.

We were on the water a short time before I realized how different touring in a boat was. There were no stoplights, turning lanes, or signs that said, "West Point – 10 miles ahead," but we saw beautiful plants and trees such as elms, sassafras, and even my namesake - the dogwoods.

I asked Mr. Sullivan if we could turn on the radio. He whispered the boat didn't have a radio. Fishermen were quiet so they wouldn't scare the fish – and fish there were. In fact, there are over 200 varieties of fish in Kentucky, with the Kentucky Bass being the state fish. I was regretting leaving my pole at home when Mr. Sullivan said we were entering Fort Knox Military Reservation. He said Fort Knox Military Reservation was 109,000 acres and covered 170 miles. It spreads over Bullitt, Hardin, and Meade Counties. Hmmm... I thought Fort Knox was about a Gold Vault. He explained Fort Knox was more than the Bullion Depository, where a large amount of the United States' gold reserves is stored. It was established in 1918 during World War I as a training camp, and became a permanent post in 1932. Though it's constantly changing, Ft. Knox has played a major role for the Army and Army Reserve. I was thinking how fortunate we were to have the best military in the world when Mr. Sullivan said we had reached West Point – and the end of the Salt River.

At the bank, we hugged Mr. Sullivan goodbye. I couldn't wait to sniff around West Point – after lunch. Mom suggested we sit on the bank and eat our sack lunch. The sandwich and Vanilla Woofers hit the spot. I now had the strength to talk about our future tour plans. I was pulling out my map when we heard the loudest whistle!

I better go! It's tough to write when I can't hear myself think! WORK AND DREAM LIKE A BIG DOG!

Chapter 3

...Se-ven, Eight, Ni-ne....... Ten!

WHEW! Ten whole sit-ups! That was exhausting, but I can already tell I'm in better shape. Without the Woody Bus, I must be prepared in case I have to walk, row a boat, or even swim to our destination. We got a doggone lucky break this time. Remember last week when we traveled the Salt River from Shepherdsville to West Point? When Mr. Sullivan dropped us off at the river bank, the four of us were unsure what we would do. While eating lunch, we heard the loudest whistle. Chloe and I covered our ears, but not our eyes. Mom and Dad pointed out that docked on the bank of the Ohio River was the *Belle of Louisville*. It was the most beautiful steamboat! I was asking Mom and Dad all kinds of questions about the *Belle* when a gentleman approached. He introduced himself as the Captain of the *Belle of Louisville*. He had heard about our bus problems, and wanted to offer us an invitation to ride on the steamboat. We couldn't believe our ears! "A ride? Really? Where are we going?" I asked. "Well," the captain said, "How about we travel west on the Ohio River to Henderson?" That was perfect! We gathered

our knapsacks, threw away our trash from lunch, and followed the Captain aboard the magnificent steamship.

The Captain told us the *Belle* is the oldest river steamboat still in operation. The 200-foot-long steamboat was originally named the *Idlewild* and first floated on the Allegheny River at Pittsburg. In 1947, the *Idlewild* was sold and its name became the *Avalon*. In 1962, the steamboat was bought by Jefferson County to become the proud and beautiful *Belle of Louisville* we all know today. On April 30, 1963, the *Belle* made her first appearance in a race against another steamboat – the *Delta Queen*. That race became a tradition. Each year on the Wednesday before the Kentucky Derby, the *Belle* and the *Queen* race up the Ohio River in the Great Steamboat Race. It was easy to see that the Belle was an important part of our state.

I'd been concentrating on listening to the Captain so much that I was completely surprised when he told us we had arrived in Owensboro. He wanted to make a quick stop so we could stretch our legs and have a snack. The Captain docked the boat and the five of us took a walking tour of Owensboro.

While walking, Chloe told us of how she had read in one of her library books that Owensboro was the third largest city in Kentucky. It was called the "City of Festivals," with its most famous festival being the International Bar-B-Que Festival. With the mention of Bar-B-Que, the captain said he had to stop to get a bowl of burgoo. "Bird goo! What in the world is bird goo?" I asked. Mom explained that it wasn't "bird goo," but burgoo, and it was a savory stew with lots of meats such as lamb, chicken, pork, and even opossum! It also had vegetables like lima beans. I love limas. I asked Mom why she had never made burgoo for us. She explained that people cooked burgoo in large iron pots outdoors. It usually took about 30 hours. That was a long time for a wiener dog to wait for supper! The Captain said that burgoo was started in the 17th century by sailors who needed a hearty meal. No wonder the Captain wanted to stop in Owensboro! By the time we had reached the restaurant, we had worked up an appetite. The burgoo hit the spot!

After our meal, we walked some more. We went to the Owensboro Museum of Science and History, the Museum of Fine Art, and toured the campus of Kentucky Wesleyan College. Our favorite part of Owensboro however was the sassafras tree. That's right – the world's largest sassafras tree is located in Owensboro. It is thought to be between 250 and 300 years old with a circumference of 21 feet. I was wondering how many birds and squirrels had made their homes in that beautiful tree when Dad and the Captain said it was time to head back to the *Belle*. I hated leaving Owensboro, but was looking forward to Henderson. Another town located on the Ohio River, it was sure to be beautiful. I couldn't help but worry what we would do when we arrived in Henderson. The Captain wouldn't be able to take us any further, so Mom, Dad, Chloe, and I would be on our own again. Would the rest of our tour be on foot? Would we be rescued once again?

Stay tuned. In the meantime, work on those sit-ups and Work and Dream like a BIG DOG!

Chapter 4

"Really, Chloe, your hair looks great!"

Hi Woody Readers! Chloe was asking me how her hair looked since she took off her helmet. I assured her she was beautiful! "Why the helmet?" You must wear a helmet when you're roller blading, riding a bike, or a motorcycle. That's right, Chloe and I had our first ride on a motorcycle – or in a side car, to be more specific.

Last week, the *Belle of Louisville* took us from West Point to Henderson. Henderson is a beautiful town located on the Ohio River. It's known for several important people, one of whom is John James Audubon. Though born in Haiti, Henderson was home to Mr. Audubon for years. He was an artist and ornithologist (someone who studies birds). He painted many types of birds. In fact, he even has a state park named after him. The John James Audubon State Park is one of 49 beautiful state parks in Kentucky. Speaking of parks, we loved Atkinson Park. Atkinson Park, is not a state park, but a city park in Henderson. Located on the Ohio River, it had swings and slides, and plenty of grass to romp in. It also had a scenic River Walk. Dad said the River Walk was a 1.2 mile trail and asked if Chloe and I wanted to check

it out. I was unsure, but Mom reminded us we had been working out, doing sit-ups, push-ups, and leg-lifts. We were up for the challenge! Looking at the clear water of the Ohio River helped pass the time. We learned on our last Bluegrass tour that Kentucky has more miles of running water than any other state except Alaska. A person could travel over 1,100 miles in Kentucky on water alone. In addition to looking at the water of the Ohio River, we also saw animals on our journey like the Cardinal, the gray squirrel, and the Viceroy butterfly. The sights made the trail go by quickly. We were tired and thirsty when we finished, but we made it! I realized my exercise program was helping me get stronger by the day!

We were celebrating with ice cold *PUPscicles* when we saw two motorcycles approaching. We watched as the riders climbed off their bikes and stretched their legs. They were dressed in leather coats, boots, sunglasses, and of course, helmets. We could tell they knew us. "Hey Woody and Chloe," they said. We barked back. They introduced themselves as Sam and Betty from Sturgis, Kentucky. When they said "Sturgis," Chloe and I remembered exactly how we knew Sam and Betty – from the West Kentucky Book Expo held at Arnold Convention Center in Sturgis. Chloe and I love signing our books at the Expo each year in October. Sturgis is known for many things – two of which are the West Kentucky Book Expo and the Little Sturgis Motorcycle Rally, which is the largest motorcycle rally in the state. Sam and Betty told us they participated in the rally and especially loved riding on the back roads of Kentucky. With that, a light bulb went off in my head! I asked if they could take us further on our tour. They were delighted! Sam explained that the motorcycles had side cars. Therefore, we could ride in the side cars. They promised to drive slowly and I was relieved. Because I was a bit of a scaredy cat when it came to riding motorcycles, the side car was perfect. Mom asked about helmets. Betty assured us they always traveled with extra helmets and proceeded to hand us one. Chloe and I put on our helmets and our own cool sunglasses. Too bad we didn't have leather jackets. Anyway, Mom helped me climb in the sidecar of Betty's motorcycle while Dad helped Chloe. While sitting in the sidecar, I noticed that Sam had a drawing on his arm. I asked what it was. Mom said it was a tattoo. My wheels started turning. Maybe Mommy would let me get a tattoo of Scooby Doo on my paw. Mom must have read my thoughts because before I could say a word she said, "Dogwood, don't even think about it!"

We left Henderson and headed south on Highway 41. We were enjoying the sights and the wind blowing against our faces. We traveled slowly through the town of Slaughters and Hanson, before making a stop in Madisonville to pick up a copy of *The Madisonville Messenger*. We had just left Madisonville when we heard sirens and saw a police car motioning for us to pull over. My heart was racing even more! Would this be the end of our tour???

Stay tuned, wear a helmet when you ride your bicycle and Work and Dream like a BIG DOG!

Chapter 5

Hi Woody Readers! No, Chloe and I are NOT in jail, nor are we in trouble! Remember when the four of us were riding in the side cars of Sam and Betty's motorcycles? We were entering the city limits of Madisonville when the police car pulled us over. Well, we were pretty frightened at first. I'd been a good boy. My only fault that day was eating some morsels of Chloe's food, but even I knew that wouldn't warrant an arrest! The policeman put my mind at ease. He introduced himself as Trooper Deron, a Kentucky State Trooper. He said he'd seen us riding in the side car and wanted to make sure we were safe. He also said that we shouldn't be afraid of law enforcers. They were here to help us, not to frighten us.

We told Trooper Deron about our Tour. He thought that was so cool! He said he had grown up in Kentucky and knew a great deal about the state. He wanted to take us further south on Highway 41. We told him we would be honored. Besides, we had never even been inside a police car. We thanked Sam and Betty for the ride and crawled inside the cruiser. While buckling my seatbelt, I noticed the lights, bells, and buttons on the dashboard. I was sure they were the buttons that made the sirens ring and the lights flash.

My mind was racing when Dad said, "Remember Woody, keep your paws to yourself!"

It was clear that Trooper Deron was a great driver and an even better tour guide. We traveled through Morton's Gap, Nortonville, Crofton, and began entering Hopkinsville. Trooper Deron explained that Hopkinsville was the county seat of Christian County. (A county seat is a town which is the capital of a county. It's where politics and government are conducted.) Trooper Deron said that Hopkinsville was the sixth largest city in Kentucky. Even though it looked calm today, it was the sight of many battles during the Civil War. Trooper Deron then took us to the Pennyroyal Area Museum. We saw a bedroom from the pioneer days, a miniature circus, an old Buick, and lots of farm tools. The museum also had information on the agriculture of Christian County, the railroad, and other modes of transportation. This was especially interesting since we had to be creative each week with our travel.

We could have stayed at the museum all day, but Trooper Deron said he wanted to show us something else unique to Christian County. Just then, my stomach growled. We stopped at Ferrell's Hamburgers for a burger and a milkshake. I ordered my burger with extra pickles. *DOGliscious!!!* The burger hit the spot. From there, we drove east on Highway 68 to Fairview, a community in Christian County. We were digesting our lunch when Mom and Dad pointed out a tall statue that looked something like the Washington Monument. Mom said it was the Jefferson Davis Monument. Jefferson Davis was born in a two-room log house in Fairview on June 3rd, 1808. He was the only President of the Confederacy. After the South was defeated in 1865, Davis was captured by the Union troops and thrown in prison for treason. He spent two years in prison, but was never brought to trial. In 1886, three years before his death, Jefferson Davis made his last visit to his birthplace of Kentucky. The Jefferson Davis Monument in Fairview is 351 feet tall and the largest concrete obelisk in the world and the fourth tallest monument in the U.S. (I made a note to self to find out what the three tallest monuments were.) The monument was completed in 1924 and celebrates the memory of Jefferson Davis.

After visiting the monument, we were sitting inside the cruiser asking Trooper Deron lots of questions about being a state policeman. He said that the Kentucky State Police was formed in July of 1948 when the Governor thought that state police could help the local sheriffs and policemen of various towns and cities in Kentucky. Trooper Deron repeated the point that the main goal of any police officer was to make sure everyone was safe.

Trooper Deron was showing us the lights and sirens of the cruiser. It was so exciting. I asked if we could see his *PAWcuffs*. He laughed and said they were called handcuffs and he would be more than happy to show them to us. In fact, he said I could try them on. Since he will need my paws, I better say goodbye for now. Stay tuned to see how I made it in the cuffs! Remember to follow the rules, thank your local law enforcers when you see them, and "Work and Dream like a BIG DOG!"

Chapter 6

Hi Woody Readers! It's Chloe! Woody sends apologies for not being able to write. Unfortunately, my brother is in the doghouse. Remember when my family traveled to Hopkinsville with Trooper Deron? At the end of our visit, Trooper Deron was showing the four of us the sirens, lights, and handcuffs. Woody, being the curious little guy he is, had to see what the handcuffs, or *PAWcuffs* as he called them, felt like. Trooper Deron put the cuffs on Woody, but as you can imagine, they were too big for his little paws. Woody looked at the cuffs and thought they were the same size as his collar, so without thinking, or asking permission, he put the cuffs around his neck and said, "Hey Chloe! Look at my new collar!" That was fine until Woody went to take off the collar and it wasn't that easy. Trooper Deron had to find the key and work to get the cuffs off Woody's neck. Once again, my little brother found himself listening to Mom and Dad talk about actions and consequences. As is always the case when Woody gets in trouble, Dad called him Dogwood and grounded him for a week. "Dogwood, no dessert or play time while we are on the road this week. In addition, Chloe will write your column for you. We love you, but you have to learn to follow our rules!"

Woody apologized to Mom, Dad, Trooper Deron, and me. We accepted his apology and all gave him a hug and kiss!

Woody not only worried about the trouble he had caused, but also about how we would get to our next destination. Trooper Deron said he had a friend in Christian County named Pete who flew helicopters. He was sure Pete would love to help. After a phone call from the cruiser, plans were set.

I asked Trooper Deron the location of the closest airport. He said the great part about helicopters was they could take off and land from almost anywhere. In fact, he was driving us to Mr. Pete's house where we would begin the next leg of our journey. This was going to be a brand new experience for us and we were thrilled!

We arrived at Mr. Pete's house, thanked Trooper Deron, and asked him for his address. We were keeping a journal of everyone's address who had helped us. We wanted to write everyone a thank-you note. With that taken care of, Mr. Pete gave us instructions about the helicopter. He told us that like a car, we must stay buckled in at all times. Mommy asked if Woody and I understood the instructions. We assured her we did, and that we would follow the rules.

As we took off in the chopper, my tummy flipped. Mommy told me to take deep breaths and I would be fine. I followed her advice and quickly began enjoying the sights from the air.

Mr. Pete said we were flying east over the southern

part of Kentucky. It was thrilling to see our beautiful state from an aerial point of view. We flew over the counties of Todd, Logan, Simpson, and Allen. We saw treetops, buildings, cows, horses, and beautiful tracts of farmland. I remembered reading in one of my library books how Kentucky ranks 37th in land size with over 37,000 miles of land. It also has approximately 91,000 farms that produce crops such as tobacco, corn, hay, soybeans, and wheat.

We also passed over a large body of water. Dad said it was the Barren River Lake. At 10,000 acres, it ran through the counties of Barren, Allen, and Monroe. Continuing, we flew over Cumberland and Clinton counties before seeing another body of water we learned was Lake Cumberland. At 63,000 acres, Lake Cumberland is one of the largest man-made lakes in the nation. It was formed in the 1940s by damming a portion of the Cumberland River. I wondered how many Kentucky Bass were in that large body of water!

We saw sights in Wayne, McCreary, and Whitley counties. Looking out the window, we saw gorgeous mountains. We learned we were flying over Bell County and those were the Appalachian Mountains. Middlesboro, the county seat of Bell, was the only city in the world to be formed by an asteroid strike. We saw the Cumberland Gap—the place Daniel Boone blazed through to get to Tennessee. We decided this was the perfect place to take a break and sniff around. Therefore, Mr. Pete is getting ready to land the helicopter. I better stop writing so I can concentrate. Stay tuned to see if

Woody is out of the doghouse. Remember to think about rules and consequences and in the words of my brother – "Work and Dream like a BIG DOG!"

Chapter 7

Boy it's great to be OUT of the doghouse – and those *PAWcuffs!* That was not a smart move. It seemed like an excellent idea, but next time I will definitely think through an idea before jumping in with all fours! Though it's never fun being in the doghouse and giving up dessert, it did give me the opportunity to spend time exercising. I did plenty of sit-ups, crunches, and jumping jacks! I was proud of my muscles before the tour, but you should see them now! (Sniff, sniff!)

The helicopter ride was a thrill. It was exciting to see part of our state from that point of view. Once we landed in Bell County and bid farewell to Mr. Pete, the four of us decided to explore the Cumberland Gap. The Gap is a major break in the Appalachian Mountains that was formed by nature. Though the history of Cumberland Gap dates back to the 17th century, it became known in 1775 when Daniel Boone was commissioned to blaze a road through the gap. Boone's Trace became Wilderness Road, and is now known as Highway 25E and 58. We walked along the shoulder while Mom and Dad held tightly to our leashes. Mom reminded us we could never be near the highway without her or Dad – and we always had to look both ways when we

Apologies to the artist
George Caleb Bingham
Jasher

crossed the street. As we walked along the edge of Highway 25E, I tried to imagine myself in a coon-skin cap, fighting a bear, just like Daniel Boone. My imagination was interrupted when a large charter bus approached. It was the longest bus I had ever seen. I always thought The Woody Bus was big – but this was huge. The bus stopped and the driver opened the door. We saw a lady wearing a blue bus-driver uniform with a big smile on her face. "Well if you aren't the two cutest wiener dogs I have ever seen!" When she said that, I fell in love!

The driver introduced herself as Miss Rose. She was taking a group of passengers to Berea. The passengers invited the four of us to join them on the trip. They didn't have to ask twice. We piled in the bus and immediately started singing one of my favorite travel songs – *"The Wheels on the Bus Go Round and Round...".* It was so much fun. By the time we finished the verse, *"The Puppy on the Bus Goes Bow Wow Wow",* we had driven from Middlesboro to Corbin on Highway 25E and were merging on the interstate. Merging on Interstate 75 North made me realize that this was the first time in our tour that we had been on the interstate. Then I saw the sign that read "No farm equipment, no pedestrians, NO ANIMALS ON FOOT!" (No wonder we had not been on the interstate.) It had been nice to be on the back roads, but the interstate allowed Miss Rose to drive faster with all of the lanes of the highway and the higher speed limit. Miss Rose said she remembered the days before the interstate. In fact, Interstate 75 was finished in June of 1970. It is the second longest north-south interstate in the nation, about 192 miles, and in Kentucky it runs from Covington to Williamsburg. I-75 and I-65 are the state's busiest interstates. I-64 however runs from the eastern part to the western part of Kentucky. Miss Rose said that you can always tell which direction an interstate runs by its number. For instance, if the number is an odd number, like 75, then it runs north and south. If the number of the interstate is an even number like 64, then the interstate runs east to west. In fact, there are over 762 miles of interstate in Kentucky. Wow! What an interstating, I mean interesting fact!

All the information kept us occupied. We were surprised when we arrived in Berea. Located in Madison County, Berea is known as the "Folk Arts and Craft Capital in Kentucky." It is also home to Berea College and welcomes plenty of visitors each year, like the group on the bus. Visitors love to come to Berea and tour the galleries and shops to see the jewelry, view the artwork, or even hear the dulcimer. With so much to do, I better sign off for now. I don't really know anything about jewelry or arts and crafts, though Chloe can make a beautiful necklace out of candy, cereal, and dog vittles. Hey, maybe Chloe could make jewelry one day.

Stay tuned to see what we have purchased in Berea. In the meantime, try to learn some interesting facts and Work and Dream like a BIG DOG!

Chapter 8

Kentucky Greetings, Woody Readers! Berea was spectacular. Chloe and I loved looking in all the shops and galleries. We saw candles, jewelry, and lots of art. We searched for wiener dog portraits, but didn't have any luck. They must have been sold out! Anyway, while visiting Berea, we spotted a taxi cab. Mom suggested that we take a cab from Berea to Lancaster to visit our friends at the Garrard County Public Library. Since we packed minimal things due to our travel situation, we had not been able to take our favorite books. We had been reading newspapers from across the state which kept us informed and entertained, but we missed our favorite bedtime stories. The library was perfect. We had been in so many libraries, but it was always exciting to see books lined across the shelves. The Garrard County library staff was so friendly. They immediately knew who we were. (I guess being two wiener dogs was a dead give-away!) Anyway, they showed us through the library and helped us find our favorite books. While Mom, Chloe, and I were browsing the shelves, Dad was telling the library director about our tour. He told her how the Woody Bus was broken and how we had to find a new mode of travel each week. The director had a great idea

—the bookmobile! We were thrilled. Honestly, we had never been in a bookmobile. The director explained that the Bookmobile Program had been in Kentucky for 52 years. In 1954, 100 bookmobiles were presented to Kentucky counties. The bookmobile is a vehicle stocked with library books that travels to the rural areas of Kentucky. It allows patrons to check out books without having to go into the main library. Today, there are over 117 bookmobiles in Kentucky, leading the nation in the number of bookmobiles. That was just one more fact convincing me that I lived in the best state of all!

The director said it would be okay if she took us a bit further on our Kentucky tour in the Bookmobile! We couldn't wait to ride in the bookmobile and look at books at the same time. Since we had to stay buckled in our seatbelts for the ride, Mom picked our favorites before we drove off. As we drove west on Highway 52, we read *Curious George, Clifford* the *Big Red Dog, Scooby Doo,* and even our own books! We were so busy reading that we didn't even notice the bookmobile had stopped. Dad informed us we were in Danville. We unbuckled our seatbelts, put our books back on the shelves in the order we found them, and gave the director a great big thank-you hug! We climbed out of the bookmobile and said hello to Danville.

We noticed we were standing in front of the Boyle County Chamber of Commerce – a great place to find information about Danville. After reading brochures, we learned that Danville was known as the "City of Firsts." It was the location of the first courthouse in Kentucky, the first Capital of the Kentucky District in Virginia, the first U.S. Post Office west of the Alleghenies, the first college in the west, the first law school in the west, the list goes on and on… In addition, Dr. Ephraim McDowell became the first physician in the world to successfully remove a tumor. Dr. McDowell made history on Christmas morning in 1809 when he performed surgery. Can you believe he didn't even have anesthesia or antiseptic? (I made a note to self to not be a scaredy cat at the vet!) The Chamber of Commerce also gave us suggestions about places we could see. We bid them farewell and walked down Second Street to visit Constitution Square.

This state historic site was the birthplace of Kentucky's statehood. Because of Danville's prime location, it became a center for political activity. In 1785, Danville became Kentucky's first seat of government. Since it was growing, it needed a meeting house, a courthouse, and a jail. Ten constitutional conventions were held at the courthouse of Constitution Square, including the meeting in which Kentucky became the fifteenth state of the Union and Isaac Shelby became the first Governor of the Commonwealth. We saw the original log courthouse, the original post office, and a replica of the original jail. Our favorite part was the Governor's Circle. Everyone was concentrating on the words *"United We Stand, Divided We Fall"* when I yawned. I was so sleepy. Mommy suggested this was a good time for a cat nap.

Therefore, I better say (yawn) goodbye for now and find my favorite blanket.

Stay tuned to see where this (yawn) little wiener dog is. In the meantime, Work and Dream like a BIG DOG!

Chapter 9

Greetings, Woody Readers! Here is a riddle for you: "What do you get when you cross a horse with the house next door?"

A nei-ei-ghbor! Get it? A Nei-ei-ghbor!!! Why am I talking about horses? Well, because Mom, Dad, Chloe, and I just rode in a horse-drawn carriage. Remember last week when we were in Danville? I was enjoying a nap when I heard, "Clip Clop, Clip Clop…." We looked up and saw a beautiful horse pulling a carriage. The driver was dressed in a top hat and bow tie. He introduced himself as Mr. Belding and asked if we needed a ride. I knew we were never supposed to accept rides from strangers, but Mom and Dad explained that Mr. Belding offered horse-drawn carriage rides as his career. Mom reminded us that she and Dad were with us, therefore it was okay. The four of us climbed into the carriage and let the horse lead the way. As you can imagine, the horse went at a much slower pace than a car, but it was a super way to see the sights. Until the railroad expansion in the late 1800s, most people traveled by horse. It was fitting that we take at least one trip on a horse since we were in Kentucky! Everyone knows that Kentucky is known for horses. Horse breeding, shows, and of course racing, have

been popular in the Commonwealth for over 100 years. In fact, horses have been an integral part of Kentucky since the frontiersman came on horseback through the Cumberland Gap. And who hadn't heard of the Kentucky Derby? The horse pulling our carriage may not have been Secretariat or Man O' War, but it was a beautiful and stout horse named Spirit that Chloe and I loved!

As Spirit led us west on Highway 150, we passed through Perryville, Springfield, St. Catharine and Fredericktown before entering Bardstown, the county seat of Nelson. Since Dad is a Nelson County native, the four of us felt like we were home. Dating back to 1780, Bardstown is the second oldest city in the state. It's known for many things—especially My Old Kentucky Home State Park. In fact, the park was the first place we arrived traveling on Highway 150. Immediately, Chloe and I began singing the chorus to *My Old Kentucky Home* – our state song. *Weep No More My Lady, Oh Weep No More Today...* Written by Stephen Foster in 1852, it has become the anthem of Kentuckians. In fact, My Old Kentucky Home State Park has a drama called *Stephen Foster – The Musical.* We noticed the park had a campsite. Dad promised us when the Woody Bus was repaired, we would come back to the park to see the musical and to camp. We were excited. I love music – and roasted marshmallows!!!

Upon exiting the park, we arrived in the center of town. We had been in the carriage for a while, and it was time to stretch. After we thanked Spirit and Mr. Belding for an excellent ride, we walked along the sidewalks. We passed the Old Talbot Tavern. The tavern is one of Kentucky's most historic inns. It hosted visitors such as Jesse James, Abraham Lincoln, Daniel Boone, and many others. The idea of a meal at the Old Talbot Tavern along with my earlier thoughts of roasted marshmallows threw my stomach into overdrive. Besides, all of the exercise I had been doing over the past few weeks definitely increased my appetite. I mentioned it to Mom and she said she had a surprise for us. Being in Bardstown, I knew it could be lots of things. Maybe it was a visit to Wickland – the home of three governors, or St. Joseph Cathedral – the oldest cathedral west of the Alleghenies, or even the Abbey of Gethsemani – a monastery built in the 1800s from a group of monks from France. Mom really surprised us when she said we were going to take a ride on *My Old Kentucky Dinner Train*. Chloe and I were thrilled. I didn't know if I was more excited about the train ride – or eating! I always heard the Dinner Train was exciting – and delicious. A piping hot *PUP-aroni* pizza sounded mighty good right about now. Mom laughed and said she didn't know if the Dinner Train offered pizza, but was certain I would love anything they served.

We are boarding the train right now. I want to be sure to get a good seat. I also have to wash my paws and practice my dinner etiquette. Tune in to see how tasty my dinner was. In the meantime, keep your elbows off the table, learn the words to our state song, and Work and Dream like a BIG DOG!

Chapter 10

Kentucky Greetings! I have one word for you—"dee-lish!" That's what I thought about the food on *My Old Kentucky Dinner Train*. Chloe and I certainly got our fill of all sorts of vittles. It was the first time we had ever eaten dinner while riding on a train. In fact, it was the first time we had ever ridden on a train.

Mom, Dad, Chloe, and I boarded *My Old Kentucky Dinner Train* in Bardstown. Now, we were no strangers to trains. I mean, we had been to the Railway Museum in New Haven, Kentucky, and there was even a train track right across the road from our house, but we had never had the need to ride one before now. The conductor of the train greeted us. Before seating us, he gave us a brief overview of trains. He said that the first U.S. railroads began operating in 1827, and by the late 1800s, trains were a vital form of transportation until the 1900s when most people started traveling by car or plane. I asked the conductor why we heard the train pass by our house several times a day. He said that trains still carry cargo across the country. He also said that trains were made up of locomotives and a series of cars. He showed us to our dining car and we took our seat. While eating our dinner and looking out the window, we noticed